THE FRIGHTENED HARE

HOLT, RINEHART AND WINSTON   NEW YORK / CHICAGO / SAN FRANCISCO

THE FRIGHTENED HARE

by FRANKLIN RUSSELL

Illustrated by FREDRIC SWENEY

Copyright © 1963, 1965 by Franklin Russell
Illustrations copyright © 1965 by Holt, Rinehart and Winston, Inc.
Library of Congress Catalog Card Number 65-14148
Printed in the United States of America
All rights reserved
97630–0316
A version of this story first appeared in the magazine COUNTRY BEAUTIFUL

A Season of Young Animals

The moon rose and the chill forest air held the first exciting smell of spring. From the spidery shadow of a young red oak came the thump of a hare's foot. From a thicket came an answering thump and then a double thump from some hemlocks. An old hare hopped three times, stood erect in the moonlight and wiggled his nose frantically.

Around him, in the forest and along its edge, were other hares. All had recently shed their white winter coats and were now brown with summer fur. They were greatly excited. One of them raced off through the trees at full speed. The old hare followed. He turned and doubled and twisted, as if to urge the other hares to close in behind him.

Suddenly, all was still. A dozen hares stood erect in the moonlight. Then they were running crazily again. The breeding season of the hares was about to begin.

The playful chasing concealed a more deadly game among the animals. During this mad moonlit night, some of the hares would fight. Fur and blood would fly when the strongest and most aggressive animals attempted to choose females for mating. The young hares fought first. The battles were vicious. Then, as if to rest from their combat, the group of hares would turn to another mad frolicsome race through the forest. The alternate fighting and racing continued night after night for almost a week. The old hare did not shrink from the fighting, but he sensed that he could not beat the younger animals. He stayed on the fringe of the fighting as long as possible.

One night a young hare challenged him with a thump of his foot and the two creatures stood in a forest clearing, facing each other. The young hare ran forward and the two animals grappled violently, biting and kicking. The old hare fell, and his body jerked with the impact of back legs kicking at his belly. He bit the young hare's ear and the animal squealed and leaped away.

Eventually the old hare was exhausted. He bled from rips and cuts. One ear was torn. As the young hare was rising for another attack, the old animal quietly disappeared through the trees and crept to the river where he would drink and rest.

Later, at the river, the old hare found his mate. She was a young female that never ventured from a small area running along the bank of the river. Forty days after they had mated, she hollowed out a nest under a fallen tree near the water and lined it with fur from her body. She bore four young hares. All were born with their eyes open and their tiny bodies covered with dark brown hair. One of them was larger and more vigorous than the others. When he was hungry, he pushed and jostled his way to his mother's milk. The young hares' coats grew sleek and acquired the fragrance of the grass in the nest. They snuggled close together and fearfully watched grasses waving in the wind. From the moment of their birth the young hares sensed that their world was filled with danger. Every movement and sound near the nest caused them to freeze into fearful watching.

It was a time of birth throughout the forest. As the old hare roamed at night, chipmunks were being born in deep burrows beneath his feet. Skunks came into the world in burrows along the river banks. Gray squirrels were born in bulky nests set high in trees. Female raccoons waddled clumsily out of hollow trees where they fed their noisy youngsters.

Once the old hare paused suspiciously, scenting
a living thing close to him. He sniffed in every
direction. Then he leaned forward. Almost at his
nose, hidden in thick grass, was a mat of fur.
As he peered at it, a dark brown eye looked
back at him. It belonged to a young cottontail
which, with three brothers and sisters,
was lying frozen into stillness waiting for
the intruder to go away.

When the old hare came loping along the river bank, he found his four young offspring venturing from the nest. They froze with fear; then they raced to safety. The young hares were gaining strength. Although they were still wobbly on their uncertain feet, they were developing into runners like their parents. Unlike young skunks, foxes and raccoons, very young hares rarely play. Their survival depends on a continual balance of boldness and caution, fear and fleetness. Above all, their safety depends on the speed of their flying feet.

The largest young hare was also the fastest, the strongest, and the most vigorous. He was the least frightened of the four youngsters. This young hare was the Runner. His strength and speed gave him a better chance for survival than most hares had in the forest.

As the young hares grew, their confidence increased and they ranged through the forest in search of food. Their mother's care for them lessened quickly. Now she often left the youngsters alone. She mated again with the old hare, and, long before the young hares were full grown, she bore another nestful of youngsters.

The Runner roamed farthest from the nest. One night he found himself alone in a strange territory, a new world teeming with enemies.

He saw a shadowy weasel speeding towards him across a moonlit clearing. He ran instinctively, ran with all the strength of his young limbs. Then, exhausted, he stopped by the tinkling river. Another shadow, another weasel, came speeding down the riverbank towards him. The Runner leaped away, fleeing with the panic of despair. The weasels were far more intelligent than he. They knew that terror-stricken hares always ran in wide circles through the forest. One weasel chased the hare while the other waited for the victim elsewhere in the forest. But the weasels could never equal the Runner's tremendous speed. He lost them that night by sheer speed and endurance.

In this way, the Runner learned about weasels. He was lucky to learn so early and survive. His brothers and sisters, now separated from him in the forest, were less fortunate. They all had an instinctive fear of flying creatures, but there was nothing to warn them against a creature which might spot them from the air and then stalk them on the ground. A hawk saw one of them on a misty wet morning. He dropped quickly out of sight into the trees and flew until he saw the hare again. Then he dropped to the ground and continued his approach on foot. When he came within a few paces of the young animal, he suddenly burst through the tall grasses and seized his victim.

Many times the Runner did not know whether he was in danger or not. But when in doubt, he usually ran. Shortly before dawn one day, he stopped by the bank of a stream and looked into the gray light of early morning. Suddenly he became aware of a tiny buzzing creature almost at his feet. It was flying quickly towards him. He sensed it was dangerous and with a great leap, he bounded away. He had disturbed a female wasp digging a burrow in the ground.

The Runner witnessed the death of one of his sisters. She had been nibbling grass, unaware that she was being watched by an owl. The owl floated silently down toward her. Suddenly the forest echoed with her screams, a series of ghastly cries. Irresistibly, the Runner felt himself drawn through the forest toward the cries. He saw other hares running with him. A scrabbling of leaves, a rustling of undergrowth, a pattering of flying feet, and six hares suddenly appeared at the edge of the forest where the owl held down his screaming victim. The hares stood tall and still in the dim moonlight. The cries died away. The owl, bent intently over the silent body, was disconcerted by the six animals standing so close to him.

He puffed out his feathers and curved his wings menacingly so that he looked twice his normal size. Then he flew to a nearby tree.

One by one, the hares dissolved into the darkness among the trees. Then the owl glided down again to where his victim lay.

One Day in the Thicket

One midday, the Runner hid in a thicket of young fir trees at the edge of the forest. He was unheard and unseen. His long, powerful back legs folded squatly against his body and his drab brown fur matched the color of the dried grass in which he was crouching.

In this season of midsummer, the Runner had met many of his enemies and he had outdistanced them. He knew the danger of the foxes. He had learned that even red squirrels might try to catch him. At night he had come to dread the silent arrival of the great horned owl, a powerful, fearless bird that caught and ate rabbits, mice and skunks.

The thicket was dense and shielded him from one of his great daytime enemies, the red-tailed hawk. This large, soaring bird frequently watched the Runner between dawn and dusk, waiting for an opportunity to swoop down at him.

At this moment, the hawk was rising rapidly into the sky above the hiding Runner. The hawk screamed loudly, and the Runner stiffened with fear.

The heat of midday pervaded the forest. The air was heavy and unmoving, and the bright wings of butterflies jerked in the hot sun. Cicadas droned endlessly. Everywhere the wasps that make nests of dried mud were building, and young birds were meeting the many dangers of their new lives. The Runner wrinkled his nose as mosquitoes hummed at his ears. They wriggled through his fur and soon he was itching with their bites.

As one of the hunted, the Runner had already learned that

he could not allow heat or biting insects to divert his atten-
tion for a moment. Though his usual time for rest was during
the daylight hours, his senses were alert even as he dozed.
Suddenly he tensed at the familiar smell of a fox. A vixen,
a female fox, was intent on her hunt for food. On her way
to a den of fox cubs, the vixen passed near the Runner's
hiding place. He lay concealed, his nostrils and whiskers
trembling as he sought the exact direction of the scent of
the fox. Again and again he sniffed. Then, without seeing
or hearing the fox, the Runner realized that the scent was
fading. It disappeared, and there remained only the familiar
smells of the enemy-free forest.

Later the Runner dozed for a moment, and then he was suddenly awake again. A new and unfamiliar scent came to him strongly but passed quickly. A great horned owl had flown silently overhead on his way into the forest.

The Runner dozed but was awakened a third time by raucous cawing. The owl had been seen by a crow. The black bird led a shrieking group of his comrades in an attack on the owl. Every crow in the forest had memories of the terrifying nighttime visits of great horned owls. No crow could be sure of his life from one moment to the next when the deep *whoo-whooing* of owls sounded in the forest at night. Now, in daylight, the crows were taking revenge. Their shrieking voices slowly faded as they drove the owl from tree to tree, farther down the banks of the river toward a distant marshland.

The heat rose out of the earth and the Runner dozed again. Then he awakened and listened intently. A pair of jays cried out in the distance. The calls faded in the hot air. The midafternoon became silent except for the drone of insects as the forest creatures retreated from the sun and heat.

The shadows in the thicket shifted slowly as the sun moved to the west. The Runner felt his appetite quickening. Ears back, he pushed through the dried grasses till he could see the treetops in the cloud-marked sky. This was a time for supreme caution. His eyes must see with acute perception, revealing his enemies in their places of concealment. He must see the faint difference between the reddish-brown coat of a fox and the reddish-brown background of the forest. He must recognize the slender outline of a hawk standing among a shadowy mass of branches.

Seeing no danger, he moved slowly forward. Then he stood erect at the edge of the thicket and his ears flipped up so that he looked very tall. He sniffed the late afternoon air. He had learned to live with a brief regard for danger; his fear came and went quickly. So when he looked up and saw the red-tailed hawk flying over some nearby beeches, he froze and became a part of his surroundings for a moment. His fear rose coldly as he waited to see whether the hawk would break his flight and dive. The hare heard the soft hiss of wind through the hawk's wing feathers as the big bird passed above the treetops.

The big bird saw the hare, but he did not hesitate. He flew on. The hare strained eye and ear for a sign of the hawk returning, but he heard only the sound of the river tinkling in the shadows. His fear vanished. He lowered himself and began cropping grass.

Suddenly he caught another scent. He was facing into the wind and it was directly ahead, a fascinating scent, rich and inviting, not dangerous. It was the scent of a female hare. He was nearly ready, in this first year of his life, to mate. He stood up, his front paws limp, sniffing so hard that his whiskers waggled and his eyes bulged.

In the meantime, the red-tailed hawk had marked the Runner's position and was now returning at a low height to attack. The hare was sniffing so intently that he did not see the hawk until the last moment. Then his bulging eyes caught a glimpse of wing tips behind him. Fear gripped him. In one convulsive leap, he hurled himself forward. At the same moment, he felt a jerk and a sharp pain in his side, but this did not slow his flight. The hawk, momentarily caught off balance by the sudden lurch of the hare, sprawled on the grass, then recovered quickly to resume the attack. But the hawk was too late; the hare had run deep into the forest.

As the last of the glow went out of the western sky, the hawk settled on a branch to spend a hungry night. The Runner, trembling with pain and shock after his escape, felt dampness on his flank and leg. This time there was no speedy recovery from his narrow escape. He panted and licked his red wound. The sky turned purple, and then the dusk became night. The Runner trembled and waited.

A Time for Sleeping

The forest moved into autumn in a shower of brilliantly colored leaves. Golden beech leaves rustled softly between gusts of wind. As the leaves fell, bursts of rain spattered from dark gray skies. This was a period of total change for the forest and for the hare. Neither would resemble its summer self by the end of the fall.

The long-healed scar on the Runner's flank was now a white slash mark with thick white fur sprouting from it. As cold enveloped the forest, the Runner's fur began to fall. His shelter became thick with the brownish hairs he was shedding. Underneath his visible coat of fur, a new coat was forcing its way through the skin. In texture it was much thicker and warmer; in color it was a pure, fluffy white. The new coat emerged first around the lower part of his body.

The hare's camouflage is timed so that he is half white and half brown during the early winter when the snow is patchy; he is all white later on in the winter when the ground is blanketed with snow.

Once the Runner had his white coat of fur, he would be more confident and carefree than before. But during this half-and-half stage, the Runner knew instinctively that he had to be quite wary. He sensed that he was vulnerable as long as the forest floor was only partially covered with snow. Only later would the thick snow and his all-white coat of fur give him the perfect camouflage.

His wariness was sharpened during this season by two events. One morning, he sensed the forest filling with a strange light. The eastern sky was a brilliant red and this soon gave way to heavy black clouds which darkened all the forest. Then came rain; at first heavy drops pattered down noisily; then a torrent soaked into the protective undergrowth above the Runner's head and sank into his fur. The noise of the rain troubled him. It roared and hissed loudly.

At the same time, he felt the dampness at his feet. Soon the dampness turned into a trickle which grew quickly. He rose from his squatting position. The trickle became a flood which brought leaves and sticks with it. Finally the Runner could bear it no longer and he burst out of the thicket and bounded away through the wet and streaming forest.

Two days later, as the ground was dried rapidly by a strong westerly wind, the Runner was troubled again. He was nibbling grass, warily watching the tree limbs lashing around him, when he felt the ground tremble. A sharp cracking noise sent him bolt upright, sniffing rapidly for danger. Then he heard a fearful crash of branches. Unable to stand the suspense, he began running. But almost instantly, he sensed he was running into danger. He turned sharply, and not a moment too soon. The forest to his left suddenly exploded into a mass of thrashing branches and leaves and the ground rocked with the impact of a falling tree trunk.

Terrified now, the Runner bolted
blindly through the trees to safety.

The transformation of the Runner's
fur was only a tiny part of the
change that was taking place in all the life
and land around him. Many animals
would slow down, become drowsy and sleep
throughout the winter. In fact, very few
creatures in the north would remain awake
and alert with the Runner through the
entire winter. Many animals would
flee to the south. Some would dig into
the earth or into the leaves; some would

submerge themselves in rivers or streams and spend the winter asleep under the water.

As the Runner dozed by day, he heard sounds of other creatures preparing for the winter. Countless thousands of birds were migrating south, some traveling by day and others by night. He heard the wild calls of hawks as they passed overhead in a flight that lasted, on and off, for three days. Unknown to him, the red-tailed hawk who had nearly killed him stood briefly in a tree near his shelter and then joined a flight of migrating red-tails.

The great bird migration brought a new danger into the Runner's life. Some birds from the Far North were migrating to his river valley to spend the winter. On one terrible night, several snowy owls patrolled the forest, seeking winter hunting grounds. The Runner's first knowledge of their arrival came when he loped through some bushes by the river and stopped to look down the stream glittering in the moonlight.

Slowly he sensed there was something wrong. He sniffed, but smelled nothing. He looked, and his eyes gradually picked out a tall shape standing motionless on a nearby stone. At first it did not resemble anything in the Runner's

experience. Then he realized it was a bird, a huge white one, and that it was looking at him with amber eyes that seemed to glow in the soft night light.

The Runner turned. Silent as moonlight itself, he slipped away upstream. Behind him he heard a soft hooting. As he ran, he saw another great white bird flying low and silently across the water. He was heading straight for the Runner. The Runner doubled back violently, tore through a thicket, stopped short and stood erect, his nostrils quivering. A third white bird—or was it the first one?—stood on a branch in front of the Runner. The Runner raced again, panic-stricken now, running with that spurt of desperation that would take him beyond the range of all forest creatures except those with wings.

He spent a night of sudden alarms. The white birds seemed to be all around him. Eventually, he sought refuge in a thicket and remained there trembling. From the forest came anguished calls as the great snowy owls continued their hunt. An animal screamed a long squawking cry that ended abruptly. A bird cackled in alarm. An owl cried "*Hoy, hoy, hoy,*" and the night of terror dragged on interminably.

The Runner could not flee the winter and had no instinct to do so. As he dozed away the days of fall, he was aware of frogs leaping past his hiding place on their way to the ponds where they would submerge themselves in mud, and sleep. Salamanders, lizardlike creatures that lived in water, migrated upstream to bury themselves in deep water.

Some creatures became suddenly more active and playful as a prelude to sleeping. A group of chipmunks kept the Runner awake one day with constant chuckering noises. They ran and scuffled playfully near the thicket in which he was hiding. They had carefully prepared themselves for the winter. All during the fall, they had carried the nuts of beech, hickory, hazel and oak into their underground burrows. Though they would spend most of the winter in a deep sleep underground, they would rouse themselves from time to time to eat some of their stored food.

The sleepers—chipmunks, raccoons, and some of the mice —sank slowly into hibernation. For days, they were drowsy. A raccoon sitting beside the river one evening yawned and yawned. This was part of a gradual slowing up of his existence. His heartbeats slowed down and his body temperature dropped. In such a state, he would be poised midway between life and death through the winter. Once he had crawled into his nest for his long winter's sleep, only warmth would awaken him.

Some other animals were intermittent sleepers, only becoming drowsy in really severe weather. The red squirrels had made special winter nests of leaves high in trees and had lined them for warmth with grasses, hair and feathers. During storms the squirrels might sleep for days in these nests. Similarly, many mice would sleep in their underground burrows only in times of bad weather.

But the Runner, perhaps the most defenseless of all the forest creatures, faced the winter without any of these methods of survival. Instead of slowing him down, the winter seemed to invigorate him. As the forest opened up around him, with boisterous winds wrenching away the last of the leaves, he gathered with some comrades and raced and chased through the rustling debris from the trees.

While playing together like this, the hares momentarily seemed safe. But they were never truly safe. As their white-blotched forms raced and scuffled through the dying light, they were watched by a pair of weasels, which, like the hares, were also turning white. (In the winter, after the weasels have a white coat of fur, they are called ermines.) Because the hares were preoccupied with their game, the weasels stole closer without being seen or scented. Suddenly the two weasels darted forward.

At that critical moment, the Runner revealed his will to survive, his strength, his speed—all within a few frantic seconds. When he saw an ermine coming at him with white teeth glistening and beady eyes gleaming, he flung himself away at top speed. Twice the ermine came close to his tail because she ran straight while he doubled and twisted. He was becoming more and more frightened, but he did not yield to his inclination to freeze in his tracks. If he did so, the ermine would catch him easily. He continued to run wildly in his determination to survive. One moment he was darting among the rocks by the river; the next instant he had hurled himself into the water. The weasel paused, perplexed, watching the Runner jerking through the water in great clumsy bounds, his head almost disappearing under the water at each kick. Despite his strange method of swimming, the Runner reached the other side, burst out of the water and fled.

As the seasons changed, so did the pattern of the Runner's coloration. By the time of the first snow, his coat was almost completely white. Patches of brown fur remained only on the top of his back.

One winter night, he was moving cautiously over the crest of a small, snow-clad, treeless hill when he froze with fear. The dreaded scent of a fox was disturbingly close. The Runner's whiskers trembled with indecision as he wondered whether or not to run. Then the Runner actually saw the animal. The fox was lying curled up, partially buried in the snow, his bushy red tail delicately covering his nostrils. His eyes were open and he was watching the terrified hare. The Runner could see the fox's body slowly tensing as he prepared to leap.

Before the fox could move, the Runner was away in a flash of speed. He never looked back. The fox did not disturb himself. He settled back in the snow and closed his eyes in sleep. The fox had no fear of any other hunter. The fox could sleep when and where he chose. The Runner, on the other hand, must outwit hunters like the fox. The Runner must also figure out how to survive the bitter cold of winter, the absence of all grass, the frozen coat of snow on all buds and tree barks. His survival would be one of the epics of the forest.

As the falling snow thickened one evening, the Runner came silently out of a thicket and stood still, almost invisible against the whiteness. Then he went silently across the snow, passing like a ghost into the first winter of his uncertain life.

Roadways in the Snow

As the winter closed around the Runner's territory, his white coat thickened for protection against the bitter cold. He stood in snowbanks during the early winter and looked squarely at hunters, such as foxes and weasels. They could not see him. Only his dark eyes showed. On bright moon-light nights, however, he carefully avoided standing in the light because hunters could trace him through the shadow cast by his body.

There was another great change in the Runner during the winter. His powerful hind legs developed strong, bristly growths of hair which sprouted out from either side of the foot pads. These more than doubled the size of both feet. The Runner could easily stand or run on the softest, deepest snow without sinking in.

A fox scented him one night and came sniffing slowly through the snow. The Runner waited in a snowbank, nose twitching. Then, when the fox was tensing for his lunge forward, the Runner jumped. His great back limbs hoisted him forward with such power that the fox got a mass of snow kicked into his face. He wallowed through the snow after the Runner, barking his frustration angrily into the forest.

Only rarely did the snow stop the Runner from his nightly wanderings. During one pale gray day, he knew from the smell of the north wind that a storm was approaching. He huddled in his shelter until dusk. When he emerged, the snow was coming down silently and thickly. It was so dark that the Runner could scarcely see anything. The wind rose and the snowflakes became smaller as they were driven into the night. The snow coated the Runner's face and whiskers. Soon the wind became a gale. The snow thickened and the roaring of the wind in the forest increased until the Runner knew that he must look for another refuge. He pushed deep into a thicket of broken branches and twigs surrounding a fallen tree until he was concealed. He pressed his body against the dead tree trunk and dozed. Meanwhile the wind roared and clattered through the empty trees and the snow made horizontal trails against the dark and angry air.

Finally, when dawn was dispersing the blackness of the night, the noise of the storm diminished a little. A gray tinge of light penetrated into the Runner's shelter. It revealed the shapes of branches and twigs piercing through the snow and ice that surrounded him. The Runner's body had given off so much heat that some of the snow had melted. Then these drops of snow-water had frozen on the walls of the tangled branches that made up the Runner's hideaway.

When the Runner woke up, he saw the icy walls all around him. With his front paws he scuffed unsuccessfully at these barriers of ice. His coat was now damp with the moisture that condensed on it from the steam of his breath. He felt the fear of being trapped. With a sudden impulse of desperation, he hurled himself forward. In one explosive second, with his powerful back legs thrusting the full length of his body forward, he burst into the open air in a shower of broken ice and scattered snow. But he had escaped one danger only to encounter others.

The Runner's flying snow-feet were no protection against the great horned owls. He dreaded hearing their hollow hooting cries that penetrated into the forest with growing frequency. Sometimes one of these big birds would let out a screaming cry that rang forever in the memories of many forest creatures. The owls were fearless and fierce, and ate anything that they could catch. One night, among the dark trees, the Runner heard a desperate struggle between a horned owl and a raccoon that had roused itself from hibernation to venture out into the frozen forest. On another night, soon after the moon had risen and bathed the trees in spectral light, the Runner saw a shape sweeping overhead. It was a great horned owl carrying the remains of a skunk that it had killed earlier in the evening and had half eaten.

The winter nights could also be a time for play. A group of hares gathered in the chill moonlight and the Runner joined them. One moment they all were still, almost invisible against the snow; the next moment, they were in frantic motion. Showers of snow were kicked up by their feet. Again, just as suddenly, the hares became still, frozen like ice. An owl had called. Long moments passed before the thumping sound of a strong back foot hitting the snow sent them racing off again.

The playing of the hares was a brief interlude in their winter lives. They lived dangerously and never knew when disaster might strike. The Runner joined a group of frolicking hares one night, but the playing was soon stopped by bitter cold which rolled in from the north and chilled them through their thick winter coats. With the cold came a steady wind which chilled the hares still more, so that the Runner was forced to take refuge under the snow. Soon after dawn, it thawed, but only briefly. Then the vicious cold again descended, freezing the melting snow on the trees into ice. As the sun rose, the icy trees glistened with sparkling prismatic colors.

The Runner emerged from his shelter to seek food. He tried to chew through the thick ice to reach the bark of the saplings, but he could not bite through the frozen overlay. As the days passed without a thaw, the hare weakened. Snow stuck to his whiskers and face. Other creatures were also suffering. He saw a pair of cottontails digging deeply into the snow in a desperate search for buried food. He watched a gray squirrel dig a tunnel under the snow to reach some buried nuts.

Then, following the freeze, came another storm. The Runner was trapped in his shelter for two days. He broke out of it from time to time, but the outside world was unrecognizable in the raging maelstrom of snow. The trees were grotesquely smothered because the driven snow had become rime wherever it hit, sticking to branches and rocks. Now the trees were so heavy with ice and rime that the forest became noisy with the sound of green wood splitting, breaking and falling. Once, the Runner was driven into the open when a branch fell across his shelter.

At the end of the second day, the Runner's life was saved by a massive thaw which enabled him to secure food. But many of the forest animals were missing. No squirrels could be seen anywhere. Gone were the occasional crow calls which had sounded in the forest. Gone also were the rattling sounds of woodpeckers driving their beaks into trees. The storm had been a catastrophe for all the forest.

Now the Runner faced a new crisis. Before the storm, he had created a series of roads through the snow because of his habit of always traveling from one food source to another by the same route. Now he had to venture into un-

marked snow and create new roads. During this time, he would be watched closely by owls, weasels and foxes which were ravenous and yearning for hare meat. The Runner loped steadily through the snow, leaving his distinctive tracks —two large prints set astride two small prints—and nibbled and chewed bark and buds. Soon his roads snaked through the forest, cutting through thickets and winding and curving in many directions. Some of his paths crossed lakes and ponds and ran along the banks of the river. Some branched and rebranched where his territory overlapped that of other hares. He often met these animals and fed with them.

A fox came loping after him one night, briefly visible as a dark mark in the snow, and maintaining his distance. The Runner spurted ahead, stopped, spurted ahead, stopped—he was unsure about a hunter that did not chase him at full speed. At the peak of his uncertainty he caught a sudden glimpse of a dark shape in a bush. The ambushing vixen leaped at him, but the Runner shot away across the deep snow, leaving her wallowing behind him.

On another night, while hiding in a thicket beside a road-way, he saw a hare being pursued by a weasel. The hare passed several times, always followed by a weasel. The hare was running on a road which encircled the Runner's territory. Apparently, two weasels were sharing the exhausting task of running the hare down. Eventually the hare left the road and crawled into a thicket near the Runner's hiding place. The Runner heard her wheezing breath. The weasels then appeared together, but they had lost the scent at the edge of the road and soon went away. Shortly before dawn, the fugitive hare died, perhaps from exhaustion. But by that time, the Runner had long since left his hiding place and had gone foraging in the night.

By now, the Runner had met most of the enemies in his life. His simple brain could understand how to elude all the obvious dangers. But there was one peril he would never understand. As he loped along a snow path one evening, he saw a strange hare half buried in some snow nearby. The animal's head was drooping forward so that his nose was touching the snow. His sides were moving quickly. Suddenly he leaped convulsively forward, fell on his side and kicked up a shower of snow. The Runner was frightened and darted away, but then he stopped and looked back. The strange hare had risen slowly and his head was drooping forward again.

This was the year of the plague, though the Runner did not realize what was happening. The plague came and went mysteriously, usually every seven or eight years. Sometimes it killed nearly every hare in the forest. Later, when the snow melted, the Runner would see many white bodies of dead hares scattered over the dark spring earth. But now he leaped on down the path through the trees, and the sick hare was left to his lonely death.

The Runner's existence was an uneasy balancing of life and death. Because he wandered constantly, having neither burrow nor comrades to protect him, he lived in sharp contrast to other forest creatures.

On the days that he ventured out in bright sunshine, he would see many deer mice and shrews running in and out of holes in snowbanks. They spent the entire winter under the snow, passing through tunnels that they had dug. They seemed much safer than the Runner. But he had seen a pair of foxes systematically digging through a snow drift and had heard the squeaking cries of the mice as their world collapsed around them and they were plucked out of the snow.

Even the cottontail rabbits that had taken over a system of burrows in the Runner's territory seemed vastly safer because they spent so much time underground. But their refuge could be a trap. The Runner saw two weasels enter the burrows one time but did not see the terror that gripped the cottontails underground. The cottontails blundered into one

another; they froze in terror; they bolted to the surface of the snowpile, sending showers of snow into the air as they fled.

The Runner paused now on the crest of a small knoll and sniffed the chill air. It was a bright, sunny winter day. The sun was so strong that it cast brilliant shimmering reflections from iced branches and from the snow itself. In the trees, chickadees searched tirelessly for insect eggs in the bark. A pair of crossbills used their strange beaks to tear pine cones apart to reach the seeds. As the hare looked down across the frozen river, he saw a fox on the far side. A cottontail was plowing up a slope towards the shiny brown trunks of some nearby beeches. As the Runner watched, the fox started across the river in slow pursuit of the rabbit. The two animals, hampered by the deep snow, were caught in a slow-motion drama in which there was none of the usual speed and action of the hunt. The strongest, most determined creature would win.

Finally, the hare could watch no longer. He turned and began running. He rushed through the snow at high speed and turned his flying body towards a thicket. He felt charged with some new and exhilarating force. He sped through the thicket with the dry sticks rattling against his sides. Even though the snow had never been deeper or the ice thicker, he had sensed that he was on the threshold of spring. He would survive the plague and see the dramatic flowering of all the country around him. Then he would find a mate and begin a new generation of hares.

Now he was racing down a broad slope overlooking the river valley, racing free on the fastest legs in the forest.

THE

FRIGHTENED HARE